Chip E. Miller
Pacific Lutheran University

Marketing

Research

Exercises

WEST PUBLISHING COMPANY
MINNEAPOLIS/ST. PAUL   NEW YORK   LOS ANGELES   SAN FRANCISCO

WEST'S COMMITMENT TO THE ENVIRONMENT

In 1906, West Publishing Company began recycling materials left over from the production of books. This began a tradition of efficient and responsible use of resources. Today, up to 95% of our legal books and 70% of our college texts and school texts are printed on recycled, acid-free stock. West also recycles nearly 22 million pounds of scrap paper annually—the equivalent of 181,717 trees. Since the 1960s, West has devised ways to capture and recycle waste inks, solvents, oils, and vapors created in the printing process. We also recycle plastics of all kinds, wood, glass, corrugated cardboard, and batteries, and have eliminated the use of Styrofoam book packaging. We at West are proud of the longevity and the scope of our commitment to the environment.

Production, Prepress, Printing and Binding by West Publishing Company.

COPYRIGHT © 1995 by   WEST PUBLISHING CO.
610 Opperman Drive
P.O. Box 64526
St. Paul, MN 55164–0526

ISBN 0–314–04737–9

CONTENTS

Section		Pages

MARKETING RESEARCH EXERCISES

Introduction

Marketing research is a fascinating and rewarding area to work in. Without it, texts on the subject would be empty of the interesting examples from the business world. Moreover, we would be far less satisfied with our choices of products if companies did not survey our tastes to see what we desire from them.

The aim of this workbook is to introduce the student to the vast collection of market research techniques and materials. When you have finished with these exercises, you should be familiar with data sources and be able to conduct credible research using secondary and primary research. We hope that you will be more comfortable with "real world" research and not just view it as theory.

In contrast to group assignments and tests fraught with time pressure, this series of problems is designed to allow you to show your own creativity and grasp of the information.

These exercises are meant to serve three primary purposes. The first is to expose you to materials that are available as secondary data sources for decision making by marketing managers. The second is to have you work with simple examples of standard market research techniques to better understand how they work, where they are inappropriate for use, and how to interpret the information gathered using them. Finally, the manual hopes to have you refresh your skills in statistics and, perhaps, regression, so that you do not forget how these important tools are employed.

Some of the information called for in these exercises may not be available in your school library. Do not be daunted. Check the local library or look into alternative sources of information. For instance, some advertising firms may have copies of the Simmons Data available. Before contacting businesses yourself, however, be certain that your instructor approves of your actions and that no other sources have what you need.

Have fun with these exercises. They are intended to stretch your mind and challenge your thinking. We wish you to go beyond mere memorization. If possible, try to pick an industry in which you already have an interest. These assignments will enable you to do the research necessary to prepare for job interviews in your chosen field.

The following is a list of industries for use by students in their research during the term. Should the instructor wish to do so, other options are available from Simmons data or Predicasts.

cigarettes	fishing equipment
housewares	discount stores
sports cars	lighting
motorcycles	armaments
shoes	department stores
batteries	games
robots	bicycles
toys	insurance
amusement parks	lasers
pest control	calculators
TV sets	photographic film
personal computers	watches
razors	jewelry
cameras	pets
eyewear	beer
restaurants	greeting cards
explosives	hotels & motels
soft drinks	helicopters
diesel engines	business magazines
furniture	recreational vehicles

MARKETING RESEARCH IN MANAGEMENT DECISION MAKING

Although not always done, marketing research should be conducted and consulted before management decisions are made. As noted in your text, the primary purpose for the existence of marketing research is to help marketing managers to make better decisions. The following scenarios are designed to give the student a look at common business opportunities. Given a good sales job by the contact, any of these might be considered a viable business venture worth pursuing. The job for the student is to critically assess each of these problems to see what else should be known before commitments are made.

ASSIGNMENT 1

Management Problem #1

You have been approached by an entrepreneur who has an idea for a new rocking chair. The chair has a mechanical back-massaging apparatus, is made of solid oak and is handmade by an American craftsman. The designer has sold them for two years at home shows and in nearby towns and even has a letter from the President of the United States praising his chair. He is interested in having the chairs mass-produced so that he can expand distribution nationally.

Current wholesale prices for a finished chair are $250. Retail prices are $375 to $450 depending on the exact configuration chosen. Preliminary talks with a furniture manufacturer in Washington indicate costs would run $285 instead of the $125 the entrepreneur has calculated is his cost to build one. Your business partner, who has some experience in retail furniture sales, says he talked to a buyer from a large department store chain who is interested in the chair.

What other information would you need before agreeing to invest $50,000 in this venture?

Be thorough in your discussion. Think about all aspects of the marketing mix as well as other issues involved in this type of start-up business.

ASSIGNMENT 2

Management Problem #2

You are doing research for a company that wishes to import glassware from China for sale in the United States. It is important that your supplier is reliable, meets your price guidelines, and that problems can be rectified quickly when they arise. Your field agent, who is a native Chinese, suggests that Shanghai is a good place to focus because it has a large, modern port and a number of glassware manufacturers in the area. What information should you obtain before selecting a supplier?

Module 2

THE MARKETING RESEARCH PROCESS

The most important step in the research process is the identification of an opportunity or problem. Until this step is carefully carried out, one should not proceed. The following vignettes represent situations where there apparently is an opportunity that should be pursued. The question put to the student is, has the research process been carried out sufficiently or is further investigation warranted?

Students should judge the research presented on the following points: accuracy, currency, sufficiency, availability and relevance.

ASSIGNMENT 3

Situation #1

One of your research associates lives in Seattle and has two teenage children, one male and one female. The son's birthday was in October and he asked for boxer shorts. A query indicates that his classmates also think that they are the latest rage. Trim fitting is out, baggy is in. Even his daughter is expressing some interest in them as everyday wear or loungewear. The researcher believes that a major ad campaign is in order so that your company can hit the Christmas market with these items and make a killing in the youth market, especially young women who are more style conscious and more extensive clothing buyers, rather than selling them to older men.

ASSIGNMENT 4

Situation #2

You have a close friend who is a Filipino who brought a new board game to your house for a party. This game proved to be a hit with the professionals you had at the party, who found the strategy and challenge more interesting than RISK and less difficult and absorbing than chess. The game is unknown in the U.S. but you believe that it would be a success because "thinking games" are always popular. Also, you read an article in MARKETING NEWS indicating that a new chain of adult toy stores is flourishing and you believe it would be the ideal outlet for such a game.

ASSIGNMENT 5

Situation #3

Your best friend has been a herpetologist and dinosaur buff since childhood. The recent resurgence of interest in dinosaurs has sparked sales of books, models, replica fossils and other products. Your friend comes to you with the exciting news that latex models of real lizards are now for sale in World of Wonder stores. He believes that monitor lizards, which look like miniature dinosaurs, will become all the rage in the pet trade because of the dinosaur euphoria and the cast models of monitors in the stores. He has a number of contacts in the reptile trade and believes that you could get exclusive rights to distribute the soon-to-be sought after lizards.

Module 3

SECONDARY DATA SOURCES

As your text has noted, one should always consult secondary data sources before conducting other research. Secondary sources are those that have already been produced for another purpose other than the current research question. They are not always available, nor are they often in the form we may wish, but they are the first place to start looking for information. In these days of ever tightening budgets, they are especially important to use.

When answering the questions for the following problems, look at them as if they were asked by the product manager or CEO from your company. Hence, you must give more than simple yes or no answers or just a number without any explanation of its meaning or units. Remember, you may have to refer to the information you have gathered to answer questions in a meeting with your superiors. Having insufficient detail will result in personal embarrassment and may have even more serious consequences.

ASSIGNMENT 6

Literature Review of an Industry

Your instructor will have assigned to you one of the industries listed in the front of this workbook or you may be allowed to select your own. You are expected to conduct a literature review of this industry using current periodicals. You will be limited to magazines, journals and newspapers. Attach a bibliography of your sources using the format chosen by your instructor.

Industry: _____

Write a brief history (100 words or less) of your industry.

_____

_____

_____

_____

_____

_____

_____

List the major competitors or top brands and their national market shares.

Competitor or Brand   **Market Share**

_____

_____

_____

What are some recent developments in the industry (e.g. new products)?

_____

_____

_____

Describe career opportunities for marketing majors in this industry.

_____

_____

_____

ASSIGNMENT 7

Review of a Company

In this exercise, you will asked to select a single company from the industry you have been assigned and collect information about it. This exercise is tantamount to what you might do if looking for a job or seeking information about a competitor for further analysis. (It is suggested that you use the *Dun & Bradstreet Million Dollar Directory* or the *Standard and Poor's Register* to find this information.)

Name of the company: _____

Corporate address: _____

_____

Telephone: _____

President or CEO: _____

If the firm has multiple product lines, select a single one and list the other officers that are involved with it by position and name.

Position	**Name**
_____	_____
_____	_____
_____	_____
_____	_____

SECONDARY DATA

The following is a list of the most common secondary data sources used in marketing research studies. You will be asked a series of questions pertaining to the industry that you have been assigned. Answer them completely and understandably, as if you were submitting a brief report to a marketing manager.

U.S. Industrial Outlook
Standard and Poor's Industry Surveys
Predicasts Forecasts
Predicasts F & S Index
Business Periodicals Index
Wall Street Journal Index
ABI Inform
Dun's Business Ranking
Commercial Atlas and Marketing Guide
Encyclopedia of Associations
Simmons Data
Thomas Register
Market Share Reporter
Brands and Their Companies

If there is no data for the question asked, fill in the space with NO DATA or N/A. Do not leave the question blank. The instructor otherwise has no way of knowing why you chose to omit an answer.

If your industry cannot be found in the source called for, ask you professor for a substitute.

DATA SOURCES & THEIR CONTENTS

Information	Source
industry prospects	U.S. Industrial Outlook Standard & Poor's Industry Surveys
value of goods & services	US Industrial Outlook
sales forecasts by product	Predicasts Forecasts Predicasts F & S Index
sales volume by firm	Dun & Bradstreet Million Dollar Directory Thomas Register Market Share Reporter Dun's Business Ranking
market share by firm	Market Share Reporter Dun's Business Ranking
market share by nation	Market Share Reporter F & S Index International or Europe
industry rank	Dun's Business Ranking
number of business locations & geographic location (by SIC code)	Census of Manufactures* Census of Retail Trade* Commercial Atlas and Marketing Guide
customer characteristics (e.g. income, media choices)	Simmons Data MRI data*
consumer buying power	Sales and Marketing Management Commercial Atlas and Marketing Guide
brand names: by company	Brands and Their Companies
general	Business Periodicals Index Wall Street Journal ABI Inform

* -- not in this workbook

products supplied:
    general   ABI Inform
                                                       Business Periodicals Index

    SIC code   Standard & Poor's Industry Surveys
                                                       Thomas Register

officers   Dun & Bradstreet Million Dollar Directory*
                                                       Standard & Poors Register*

company size (no. of employees)   Dun & Bradstreet Million Dollar Directory*
                                                       Standard & Poors Register*

affiliations   Encyclopedia of Associations

* -- not in this workbook

ASSIGNMENT 8A

U.S. Industrial Outlook

This volume contains annual forecasts of the U.S. economy made by the Department of Commerce. Information is listed by SIC code. Major groups have 2 digit codes, industry groups 3 digits and industries 4 digits. Output is listed by individual factory and by industry, with much information coming from the *Census of Manufactures*. The value of goods and services is given in current dollars and constant dollars. The latter allows you to compare real changes in output over time.

You will be asked to investigate your industry and answer the following questions about its current situation and future prognosis.

Write the name of your industry here. _____

List the SIC code for your industry _____

Is your industry regulated by any federal agency? If so, what is the name of that agency and which larger government body does it belong in? (e.g. the Food and Drug Administration [FDA] is part of the Department of Agriculture)

Regulating agency _____

Overseeing department _____

_____

Summarize the current situation for this industry.

_____

_____ ; _____

_____

4. Describe the short term and long term projections for your industry.

Short term: _____

_____

Long term: _____

_____

5. What is the outlook for international trade in this industry?

_____

_____

_____

6. How much was spent on research and development (R & D) in the last year in this industry?

_____

7. What significant events occurred in this industry during the last year?

_____

_____

ASSIGNMENT 8B

Standard and Poor's Industry Survey

These surveys are assembled annually, with revisions during the year for the current analyses. Both Basic and Current analyses of industries are offered. These examine the prospects of an industry, its trends and its problems. The comparative company analysis allows the reader to compare growth in sales and earnings of leading companies.

Write the name of your industry here: _____

What is the SIC code for your industry? _____

Who are the major companies and what are their ranks by sales volume?

Company   **Rank**   **Sales Volume**

_____

_____

_____

What are the major products in your industry? To whom are they important (e.g. government, other industry [name them], consumers).

Product   **Used by**

_____

_____

_____

List the important events that have happened this year in your trade line.

_____

_____

_____

Which firms in your industry figure prominently in the S&P survey? List their names here, with a brief note of why they were mentioned.

_____

_____

_____

_____

_____

_____

What is the outlook for this industry both in the U.S. and abroad? Be more precise than just "good" or "bad". Describe expected breakthroughs, new trading alliances or other major events anticipated. On the foreign notes, indicate for the most important nations what the outlook is, if the data are present.

U.S. _____

_____

_____

_____

Foreign: _____

_____

_____

_____

Write an abstract of the survey (150 words or less). This should include such details as the major players, the outlook for the industry, which foreign countries figure prominently in the report and which products are in ascent or decline.

_____

_____

_____

_____

_____

ASSIGNMENT 8C

Predicasts Forecasts

This data source compiles forecasts on products, markets, industry and economic aggregates for the U.S. and North America. The information is published quarterly, with a list of sources given in the index. Forecasts are grouped by 7 digit SIC code.

Give the name and the SIC code for your product:

_____

How does this SIC code differ from other uses you have seen?

_____

Describe the activities for your product over a 3 year period. What pattern do you see?

_____

_____

What do B, S and L stand for?

_____

What do f, h, k and z mean in the time period section?

_____

Name 2 different sources for your forecast.

_____

_____

What annual growth is projected?

_____

ASSIGNMENT 8D

Predicasts F & S Index

This index contains company, product and industry information from over 750 business-related publications and reports. Included is information on mergers and acquisitions, new products, technology developments and socio-political factors affecting business.

The index comes in 2 volumes: the industries and products information is found in the green pages and the company information is in the white pages.

Give the 3 or 4 digit SIC code for your product._____

List the year of the index you are using. _____

Give the 7 digit SIC code and name of your product.

_____

What is happening with this product?

_____

_____

What future developments are discussed?

_____

_____

List 2 companies involved with this product.

_____

_____

Describe other events that pertain to one of these 2 companies. How will they fare based on these reports?

_____

_____

_____

Conduct the same search in either the international or European edition of this index.

Which areas does the International volume cover?

_____

_____

How does the global scene differ from the U.S.?

_____

_____

_____

Which company or country is in the lead technologically? in sales?

_____

_____

Which countries and companies are major global players?

_____

_____

ASSIGNMENT 8E

Business Periodicals Index

This index is published monthly, with an annual cumulation each August. The publication lists a wide array of articles of interest to business. These articles are given in alphabetical order, without regard to SIC or other codes. Its scope covers both academic journals and the popular press. The periodicals indexed are listed in the front of each volume.

Write the name of your industry here:

_____

What alternative titles does the index suggest that you look under in addition to marketing? (look to the **see also** list)

_____

Identify 3 articles that pertain to your topic, including one that discusses a single company in your industry. Give proper bibliographic citations for each of them below.

_____

_____

_____

_____

_____

_____

Summarize the contents of one of the articles.

_____

_____

_____

_____

_____

ASSIGNMENT 8F

Wall Street Journal Index

This index contains information from the Eastern edition of the *Wall Street Journal* in two separate sections. One deals with corporate news and the other deals with general news. The corporate news is arranged alphabetically by company or organization name. General news is alphabetical by person, product or geography. Approximately 4000 headings are used. The index comes in 8 monthly and 4 quarterly volumes. Stock tables are not included.

How are the geographic locations indexed?

_____

What does the citation 5/18-9; 5 mean?

_____

What year WSJ did you use? _____

Write your topic name: _____

What else is your topic listed under? _____

_____

What is an important issue in your industry? Cite 2 articles dealing with it and summarize the contents of one.

_____

_____

_____

_____

_____

Cite one article dealing with your topic in a foreign country.

_____

_____

How do these articles compare with others you have read in other publications? Do the findings support or contrast with those of other writers? How are these articles in terms of depth and timeliness?

_____

_____

_____

_____

ASSIGNMENT 8G

ABI Inform

ABI Inform is a computerized database containing a wide range of business periodicals. Abstracts are available for each article cited. Keywords are used to search the database but must be used carefully. Your reference librarian should be consulted for assistance.

List your product or industry here:

_____

What key word did you use first?

_____

How many cites did you get?

_____

Narrow your search parameters and rerun 2-3 iterations. Describe your changes here and how it reduced your citations.

_____

_____

What advantages does ABI give you? _____

_____

_____

What disadvantages are there? _____

_____

_____

Summarize one interesting article you found.

_____

_____

_____

ASSIGNMENT 8H

Dun's Business Ranking

These annual volumes rank over 25,000 public and private businesses. One may locate information by state, SIC code, nation or size (sales volume or employee size). SIC codes are 4 digit.

What are the top 5 businesses in the United States?

Business   **Sales Volume**   **SIC**

_____

_____

_____

_____

_____

Within the state you have been assigned, give the top 3 businesses, their rank in industry and their sales volume.

Business   **Sales Volume**   **Rank**

_____

_____

_____

List the top 3 businesses in your industry and their sales volume. (If your industry is not given in the book, either select another or use a 2 digit SIC code that corresponds to your original industry.)

Business   **Sales Volume**

_____

_____

_____

What are the top 3 foreign businesses or private businesses? If foreign, give the country of origin.

Business   **Foreign or Private?**

_____

_____

_____

How do the foreign/private firms compare with U.S. public firms in terms of sales volume and size?

Business   **Sales**   **Size**

_____

_____

_____

ASSIGNMENT 8I

Commercial Atlas and Marketing Guide

This annual guide is broken into 6 sections--1) US and metropolitan maps 2) transportation and communication data 3) economic data 4) population data 5) state maps 6) index of statistics and places by state. There is also information on sales and population by 3 digit zip code and county sales data.

Your instructor will assign a state for you to work with.

State: _____

How many SMSAs (standard metropolitan statistical areas) are found within this state? Identify up to 3 of them.

_____

How many CMSAs (consolidated metropolitan statistical areas) are there? Identify up to 3 of them.

_____

What is the largest SMSA in this state? What is its population?

_____

Locate a trading area within your state. Is its center within the state or located in another state? Where is this center?

_____

Does your state have a corporate leader? If it does, what is its name and which industries is this firm in?

_____

ASSIGNMENT 8J

Calculating and Using a Buying Power Index

You have been hired by WalMart to assist in determining which cities it should target for its continued expansion. You are asked to rank order the cities in the target state based on their total sales potential. Your ranking will be arrived at by using the Buying Power Index (BPI) found in the annual "Survey of Buying Power" in *Sales and Marketing Management.*

Your instructor will assign you a state in which to work.

STATE _____

CITY   BPI

1. _____   _____

2. _____   _____

3. _____   _____

4. _____   _____

5. _____   _____

6. _____   _____

7. _____   _____

8. _____   _____

9. _____   _____

10. _____   _____

2. Explain what the difference in BPI among the various cities means.

_____

_____

_____

3. You are also asked to develop a special index for the top 5 cities on your list. According to the previous experience of WalMart, the three principal product categories should be weighted as follows. The weights are assigned based on proportion of corporate sales represented by each category.

Product Type	Weight
Drugs	.1
Food	.2
General Merchandise	.7

Use the worksheet below to compute your custom index. Use the rank from the previous section for the city designation below. All sales are in thousands of dollars.

City	Food ($000)	A Food x Weight	General Mdse. ($000)	B General Mdse. x Weight	Drugs ($000)	C Drugs x Weight	Sum A+B+C	Index (A+B+C)/T
___	___	___	___	___	___	___	___	___
___	___	___	___	___	___	___	___	___
___	___	___	___	___	___	___	___	___
___	___	___	___	___	___	___	___	___
___	___	___	___	___	___	___	___	___

T = Total = _____   1.00

36

3. Did you discern any difference in rank order using the two different indices? What occurred? What difference would this make to a market researcher using these indices? What advice would you give them, if any?

_____

_____

_____

ASSIGNMENT 8K

Encyclopedia of Associations

This annual encyclopedia supplies details on almost 23,000 national and international nonprofit, trade and professional associations, sports, hobby groups and others. It is arranged by subject. Geographic and executive indices are available. Information supplied includes association name, address, number of members, services and publications.

Write the name of your industry here:

_____

What keyword(s) are associated with it in the encyclopedia?

_____

Write the section that your industry is located in.

_____

Select one organization dealing with your industry and provide:

Name of the organization:

_____

_____

Year founded: _____

Membership: _____

Affiliated with: _____

_____

Publications: _____

_____

Meeting schedule: _____

ASSIGNMENT 8L

Simmons Study of Media & Markets

These data are a study of media and markets. The results are from a large sample of U.S. adults and can be projected to the population over 18 in the lower 48 states. You may learn who reads what magazines and newspapers, who watches which shows on TV and who listens to what radio format. It also provides details on their income, age and education. Finally, it cross references the type of users of a product or service with the best media to reach them.

Your instructor will assign you one of the product series volumes. Select one product from the volume and answer the following questions.

Name of your product: _____

Is your product listed by males, females, or a combination? If a combination, what does it consist of? (e.g. archery is adults and males, with no separate female data)

_____

How many used or purchased your product within the last 12 months?

_____

What percent are in the highest use category? What is it?

_____

What age group has the largest number of people? (watch the number here--read the column heading)

_____

What region of the U.S. has the most participation?

_____

Which household income is most prevalent? _____

Which household size is most common? _____

Look at column A. What 3 magazines are best to advertise in based solely on reader numbers?
List them and their circulation numbers.

_____

_____

What radio format is best to reach your target audience? worst?

Best_____Worst_____

What 2 evening TV shows would we choose based solely on viewer numbers? List the viewer
numbers for each program selected.

_____

Which magazines and TV programs would you recommend based on the content to most
efficiently reach your target audience?

Magazines (choose 2)

_____

TV programs (choose 2)

_____

Why did you select these? How do they differ from the ones chosen strictly on numbers of viewers/readers?

_____

_____

ASSIGNMENT 8M

Thomas Register

This annual publication comes in 3 sections with multiple volumes--product and service, company profile, and catalogs. The company section lists assets, company executives and office locations. The catalog section includes reproductions of company catalogs. Products and services are listed alphabetically and use the modified noun system (e.g. motors: electric). Volume 17 uses a normal alphabetical index.

Your industry here: _____

What is the largest firm to supply you? _____

_____

How can you tell? _____

_____

What is the firm's rating?   In which volume did you find this information?

_____

Does this firm have a display ad? If so, please attach a copy and critique the ad. If not, what would you recommend it look like?

_____

_____

_____

What trademarks and brand names does this firm use? Where did you find this information?

_____

_____

Give the city and state of the closest branch office of this firm. Which volume was this in?

_____

ASSIGNMENT 8N

Market Share Reporter

This volume is a compilation of market share reports from business periodical literature and brokerage reports. It is limited to published market shares, so the results are not exhaustive. It is broken down by corporate market share, institution, brand share and product share. Product share is subdivided by components (e.g. refrigerators, ranges, dishwashers). Both 2 digit and 4 digit SIC codes are used. Information is available on more than 5200 companies, 1700 brands and 2700 products or services.

List your SIC code and area of interest:

_____

What types of product are discussed here? List them.

_____

_____

Report the sales by brand as shown.

Brand   **Sales**

_____

_____

_____

_____

What are the leading firms in your industry and their respective ranks?

_____

_____

_____

_____

_____

List one more fact that you found interesting and why it was so.

_____

_____

_____

_____

ASSIGNMENT 80

Brands and Their Companies

This publication is especially useful for trade name searches. It lists over 282,000 brands from 51,000 manufacturers and distributors. Brands are listed alphabetically, with companies in a separate section. Over 120 industry-specific sources are cited. Both public and private firms are listed.

Write the name of your industry here:

_____

What are the brand names used by the top 3 firms in your industry? List only those brand names for the products in your area. Do not include brand names for subsidiaries or divisions.. (For example, Pepsico owns Frito-Lay. You should only list soft drink brands of Pepsi, not Frito products.)

Firm name #1_____

Brand names_____
and their
products _____

_____

_____

Firm name #2_____

_____

Brand names _____
and their
products _____

_____

Firm name #3 _____

Brand names _____
and their
products _____

_____

_____

What similarities do you notice between the brand names, if any?

_____

_____

_____

_____

Now look at one of the less prominent firms in your industry.

Firm name #4_____

Brand names _____
and their
products _____

_____

_____

How do the brand names for its products differ from those of the leaders?

_____

_____

_____

_____

ASSIGNMENT 8P

International Business Exercises

With the increasing importance of international trade, one should also become familiar with secondary data sources that supply information for countries other than the U.S. Be sure that you write down the name of the publication you used and the year. If business reference does not have what you are looking for, check government documents.

1. Locate the leading export item from Panama.

2. Find the SIC number for Motor Vehicle Bodies. What is it? Does the U.S. have any subsidiaries in Brazil with this SIC number? List one.

3. What is the address of the Toyota subsidiary, Toyota Tsusho America Inc., located in the U.S.?

4. In September of 1988, a newspaper article discussed the Japanese stock decline resulting from Hirohito's failing health. Name the newspaper and give the exact date of the article.

5. List a Japanese company that might want to import logs from the U.S. to Japan. Give the full address and list the chief executive officer.

6. Poland is interested in doing business with the U.S. Suppose that you wanted to advertise in the largest circulation daily paper in Warsaw. What is its name and circulation figure?

7. Pratt and Whitney Aircraft has operations in other countries. In September of 1988 it announced plans to extend its engine support facility located in what country? Give the citation for the magazine or newspaper that reported this item.

Module 4

USING THE CENSUS

ASSIGNMENT 9

Store Site Selection

The data collected by the Bureau of the Census are vast and extremely useful for many purposes. This exercise will introduce you to that database.

Your instructor will assign you an SMSA to work with. You will need to search the General Characteristics of the Population and Income Characteristics of the Population tables to complete this exercise.

You have been contacted by a sporting goods store to determine a site for its new store. Past research has indicated that their target population has the following characteristics:

25 to 34 years old

income between $25,000 and $34,999

children under age 18

Using the worksheet that follows, identify those census tracts that look like the most promising areas to open the new store. Be explicit about why you chose the tracts that you did--tell the management team exactly what criteria you used to determine what areas were most suitable.

Census Tract No.	Census Tract Population		Person 25 - 34				Person $15,000-$24,999 Income		Families in Census Tract			Targeting		Summary	Would You Recommend As a Target Tract
No.	Total	Percent	Male	Female	Total	Percent	Total	Percent	Total	Number with Children Under 18	Percent with Children Under 18	Check If Meet Age Criterion	Check If Meets Income Criterion	Check If Meets Children Criterion	

Module 5

DESCRIPTIVE RESEARCH

What does 220 mean to you?

Most of you assume that means weight, and that weight is in pounds. But a 220 could be an engine size in either cubic inches (for a car) or cubic centimeters (for a motorcycle). It is also the caliber for a rifle and voltage in Europe and Asia.

The important point is, be sure you know what you are listening to and know what the units of measurement are.

What is she, a 20 footer?

This might mean either a boat or a python, depending on who is talking.

What's a 10?
1) a beautiful woman
2) a top score in gymnastics
3) a pistol caliber

38-23-36 is...

a locker combination

Let's assume your parameters for a market segment are as follows:

> male, 25-40
> enjoys outdoors
> social club member
> frequent traveler
> believes clothes make the man

What do you envision as your customer?

Now turn the page for what market research turned up as a stereotype of this segment.

How many of you thought of THIS person? Description still fits, doesn't it?

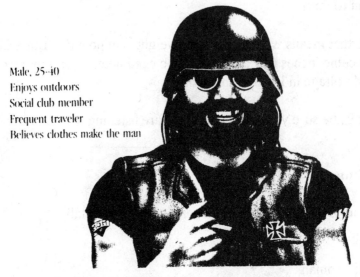

OBSERVATION RESEARCH

This section deals with observation research, another area that, like descriptive research, is often given inadequate attention. The proposed exercises present you with 2 situations. The first gives a wealth of data about 2 individuals and you are asked to predict what products these persons will like. The situation is akin to sifting through data from sales reps concerning their customers.

ASSIGNMENT 10a

OBSERVATION EXERCISE
An Office Visit

You have been provided the following descriptors on 2 individuals. Your task is to determine from this data how appropriate it would be to sell certain products to these persons. Write a short explanation for why you feel the person would desire your product and what type would be appropriate. Be fairly detailed about the type of product that is best, if any seems appropriate. Also, you should consider such details as the amount of product that would be consumed and even where that consumption might take place.

Example: Person A would be an ideal candidate for an expensive, manually operated 35mm camera that allows them to produce their own pictures and not be limited by a "do-all" that is completely automatic. Also, based on the products visible in their office, they appear to be less price sensitive and would buy a more expensive camera. Impressing associates with a fine camera might also be a factor.

Person B seems to be very practical and would like a fully automatic camera that doesn't get in the way. They might not even care about a camera at all but would just buy postcards or slides to avoid the hassle. Probably doesn't care what people think about the camera he carries.

Products

computer	games	vehicle
hunting/fishing trip	sports club membership	restaurants
	TV/VCR	

PERSON A

Fortune
Wall Street Journal
7 Secrets of Successful People
Guerrilla Marketing
Smithsonian
Natural History

Robert Ludlum hardbacks (intrigue & spy novels)
Tom Clancy hardbacks

Roget's Thesaurus (hardback)

glass & steel desk
black marble desk accessories
gold ballpoint pen

stereo system tuned to classical music station

interesting artwork framed and adorning walls
   oil painting entitled "The Bookworm"
   art print by Durer, "Knight, Death and the Devil"

PERSON B

Reader's Digest
Guns & Ammo

local newspaper

Time-Life World War II series
Conan short stories (sword & sorcery paperbacks)

paperback dictionary

plastic desk organizers

plastic Papermate pens

clock-radio tuned to oldies station

framed posters on the walls
   Frazetta (artist for Conan books)
   Nagel

ASSIGNMENT 10b

OBSERVATION EXERCISE 2
A Shopping Trip

This exercise is a field experience. You will be sent out to look at various malls or shopping areas in the city and asked to describe the character of the area and the type of people who shop there. Alternatively, if there are not malls or multiple shopping areas, you will be assigned to do the same for different types of stores that carry the same products. For example, the patrons of K-Mart (a discount retailer), J.C. Penney (a mid-range soft goods retailer) and The Bon Marche (a slightly upscale department store) could be compared.

When conducting your study, you should note such characteristics as:

Age of the shoppers

General attire

Number of children with shoppers

Types of cars most often seen (foreign/domestic; age; appearance)

Stores in the mall/shopping area besides "anchor" stores like Penney's or Nordstrom's--what are they like? what do they sell?

What other characteristics are seen? Is there a food plaza in the mall? What is it like?

Module 6

MATCHING DATA GATHERING METHODS AND RESPONDENTS

The severe budget constraints prevalent in today's business climate demand that the researcher be able to determine the most appropriate data collection method. Also, as others have pointed out, it is the quality of the data that is more important than the sample size. Hence, you will be asked to decide how to get the most rich information from the groups shown.

ASSIGNMENT 11

The following is a list of various groups and potential research topics. For each group, decide whether personal interview, telephone interview, or mail interview would be the most effective data collection method. State your reasons for each choice.

1. First Grade teachers in 5 local school districts. Effectiveness of a new learning tool.

Data collection mode:

Reasons for use:

2. Television viewers in your city. Opinions on a new local television news show.

Data collection mode:

Reasons:

3. Voters nationwide one day before a senate vote on a new tax on tobacco products.

Data collection mode:

Reasons:

4. Patrons of a major hardware store chain. Preferences in tool brands.

Data collection mode:

Reasons:

5. Movie patrons--taste preferences between air-popped and oil-popped popcorn.

Data collection mode:

Reasons:

6. Travel agents in the larger cities in your home state. Changes in vacation trends.

Data collection mode:

Reasons:

7. AARP members. Quality of services for the elderly.

Data collection mode:

Reasons:

8. Teenagers. Preferred athletic shoe brands.

Data collection mode:

Reasons:

9. Shoppers in a local grocery store. Use of coupons.

Data collection mode:

Reasons:

Module 7

QUESTIONNAIRE DESIGN

Students get far too little practice dealing with questionnaire design and correction. It is as much art as science, and requires some creative thinking. Two exercises are presented here. The first asks you to repair a set of random questions selected from several questionnaires. All are poorly worded or misleading--there are no trick questions that have no problems associated with them. The second exercise is a complete questionnaire that has numerous flaws and may require rewriting. Placement of questions, question design, sufficient number of questions for a given topic area, and category overlaps will all be included in this exercise.

Your first attempt at questionnaire design is often difficult and not very successful. Students in most principles of marketing classes may never learn to design questionnaires because they are running a simulation that does not require them to learn the basics of marketing research before they begin making marketing mix decisions. Hence, these exercises are designed to help you identify problems with survey instruments so that you can critique your own efforts prior to bringing them to the professor. It will also enable you to later understand how and why research by your own or other companies can be misleading and must be checked from the data gathering stage first.

ASSIGNMENT 12

Random Question Sheet

Critique these questions as completely as possible. They are taken from a number of research questionnaires, but all are real and all have some flaws.

1. Do you have soda with your mixed drinks?   yes   no

2. Do you usually have beef or chicken at dinner? yes   no

3. How much do you usually pay for a dozen eggs?

    a. less than 75 cents
    b. $.75 to $1.00
    c. $1.00 to $1.15
    d. $1.15 to $1.25
    e. over $1.25

4. Do you prefer large, inefficient engines in your car?

    yes   no

5. Is a transverse mounted engine something you would like in your next car?

    yes   no

6. Are you still beating your wife?

7. How long has it been since you last had a drink?

    a. today
    b. yesterday
    c. 2-4 days ago
    d. more than 5 days ago

8. How much alcohol do you drink in a month?
    a. none
    b. 1-4 cans of beer
    c. 5-12 cans of beer
    d. 13-24 cans of beer
    e. more than a case of beer

9. How likely is it that you would go to Greece on your next vacation?

1	2	3	4	5	6
not at all likely					very likely

10. What kind of car would you like to purchase next?
   a. sports car
   b. sedan
   c. station wagon
   d. utility vehicle

ASSIGNMENT 13

Questionnaire Design

An inventor has designed a new product that he feels has great sales potential among golfers. This item is a cooler sleeve that attaches to the side of one's golf bag and has a spring loaded plunger so that drinks are always at hand when one opens the cooler. He has no idea of how to determine whether his product will sell and has tried to put together a marketing research questionnaire on his own. A sample of the questionnaire follows.

Your job is to fix his efforts so that he can determine a marketing strategy for his product. Discuss the shortcomings of the survey he has put together and design one of your own that meets the needs of this inventor.

1. What is your age? _____

2. What is your sex? _____

3. What was your disposable income last year?

a. less than $15,000

b. between $15,001.00 and $23, 000.00

c. $23,000 to $37,000

d. over $37,001

4. How often do you play golf?_____

5. Do you drink when you play golf?   yes   no

6. Do you own a golf cart?   yes   no

7. How many children are in your family?

a. none

b. 1-3

c. 4 or more

8. What color would you like to have in a golf bag accessory?

a. black

b. blue

c. dark green

9. Where do you play golf?

a. public course

b. country club

10. Would you buy a drink cooler for your golf bag?

      yes   no

11. What is your occupation?

a. doctor

b. lawyer

c. blue collar

d. student

e. unemployed

f. manager

Please give us your name and phone number so that we can call later with details about our product.

Module 8

DATA COLLECTION

Most of you became only vaguely familiar with statistics before entering marketing research, and many did not work with such issues as sample size at all, because the problem sets provided that information. Now it is important that you understand how those sample sizes were determined and why.

ASSIGNMENT 14

Sample Size Problem

Based on a client's requirements of a confidence interval of 99 percent and acceptable sampling error of 2 percent, a sample size of 500 was calculated. The cost to the client would be $20,000. The client replies that the budget for this project is $17,000. What are the alternatives?

ASSIGNMENT 15

Quota Sampling Exercise

As noted in your text, there are times when it is advisable or required that you do not do a random sample. This practice set will help you to see how a quota sample is drawn.

Your instructor will assign you a state capital to use as the basis for your quota sample. Your client is interested in finding out about the opinions of the people in the city but wants to be certain that certain groups are adequately represented in the sample. Your sample size is 600. The information can be found using the United States Census.

POPULATION FIGURES

1. The first step is to record the population figures for the groups in question. Your matrix will look as follows:

	Whites	Blacks	Hispanics	Row Total
18-24				
over 65				

Enter the population for each segment.

2. Now compute the proportion value for each cell. For example, divide the value in cell #1 by the total population of cells 1-6. Convert those numbers to percentages.

	Whites	Blacks	Hispanics	Row Total
18-24				
over 65				

3. Finally, determine the number of individuals in each cell by multiplying the percentages obtained in #2 by the sample size of 600.

	Whites	Blacks	Hispanics	Row Total
18-24				
over 65				

Module 9

DATA ANALYSIS

ASSIGNMENT 16

Dealing with Missing Data

In this exercise, you will be faced with a common problem--some of the respondents did not fill out their survey completely. Your job is 1) to determine whether or not to fill in the missing data 2) ascertain what impact is had by various approaches to dealing with missing data.

You have been asked to prepare a small sample of responses from young people concerning their reaction to mandatory national service. The dependent variable was a semantic differential with the following scale codes:

Not in 1   2   3   4   5   6   7   In favor
favor

You have been given a sample of 10 responses, the results of which are shown below. Demographic information is included with this data.

Person	Service	Age	Income
1	7	22	17,600
2	3	--	15,500
3	4	21	20,500
4	5	22	--
5	-	26	26,000
6	5	23	--
7	5	--	35,800
8	1	22	--
9	6	23	15,500
10	4	27	31,600

Compute the mean of each variable--service, age, income--using each of the following strategies to deal with the missing data.

1. **Ignore missing data**

service =

age   =

income =

2. **Eliminate cases with missing data**

service =

age   =

income =

3. **Impute a value for missing data**

(a) **Random assignment**

Use a random number table to select values to fill in the gaps in the table.

service =

age   =

income =

Explain how you arrived at the random income amount.

_____

_____

(b) Interpolate using a value from a similar case

service =

age   =

income =

(c) Insert the mean obtained from valid cases

service =

age   =

income =

4. Summary Table--Comparison of Missing Data Strategies

	Means		
Technique	Service	Age	Income
1. ignore missing values			
2. eliminate cases			
3a. impute random numbers			
3b. impute similar cases			
3c. impute mean			

Discuss your findings. What do you conclude?

_____

_____

_____

Notes on Statistics

We often referred to our numerical analysis classes as "sadistics". Actually, with a little work, the formulae and the output become familiar and are easy to work with. The problem lies in practicing with them until one understands what is useful when. A chart follows this page with guidelines of what tests are appropriate for which types of data.

It is most important that the student be able to take the computer printouts provided by the statistician and explain what they mean. Thus, the comprehensive case dealing with airline preference has been largely completed for you. You will be as to provide explanations as to what the data analysis means. You will be expected to be able to work with the statistics package on your own for the remaining cases, using the airlines case as your guide for commands and syntax for SPSS/PC+.

AREA OF APPLICATION	SUBGROUPS OR SAMPLES	LEVEL OF SCALING	TEST	SPECIAL REQUIREMENTS	EXAMPLE
Hypotheses about frequency distributions	One	Nominal	X^2	Random sample	Are observed differences in the numbers responding to three different promotions likely/not likely due to chance?
	Two or more	Nominal	X^2	Random sample, independent samples	Are differences in the numbers of men and women responding to a promotion likely/not likely due to chance?
	One	Ordinal	K–S	Random sample, natural order in data	Is the observed distribution of women preferring an ordered set of make-up colors (light to dark) likely/not likely due to chance?
Hypotheses about means	One (large sample)	Metric (interval or ratio)	Z-test for one mean	Random sample, $n \geq 30$	Is the observed difference between a sample estimate of the mean and some set standard or expected value of the mean likely/not likely due to chance?
	One (small sample)	Metric (interval or ratio)	t-test for one mean	Random sample, $n < 30$	Sample as for small sample
	Two (large sample)	Metric (interval or ratio)	Z-test for two means	Random sample, $n \geq 30$	Is the observed difference between the means for two subgroups (mean income for men and women) likely/not likely due to chance?
	Two (small sample)	Metric (interval or ratio)	One-way ANOVA	Random sample	Is the observed variation between means for three or more subgroups (mean expenditures on entertainment for high-moderate and low-income people) likely/not likely due to chance?
Hypotheses about proportions	One (large sample)	Metric (interval or ratio)	Z-test for one proportion	Random sample, $n \geq 30$	Is the observed difference between a sample estimate of proportion (percentage who say they will buy) and some set standard or expected value likely/not likely due to chance?
	Two (large sample)	Metric (interval or ratio)	Z-test for two proportions	Random sample, $n \geq 30$	Is the observed difference between estimated percentages for two subgroups (percentage of men and women who have college degrees) likely/not likely due to chance?

ASSIGNMENT 17a

Regression Basics

Regression analysis will allow you to determine whether a relationship between variables exists, as well as the direction and amount of change one can expect in one variable when other variables change.

The following situation concerns a company with national product sales. It has 20 regional distribution centers with roughly similar revenue generation. A new product is being test marketed in 10 regions, with differing levels of advertising in each. The table below shows the region, advertising expenditure and sales volume.

Region	Advertising ($ 000)	Sales ($ 000)
1	20	160
2	10	120
3	30	220
4	16	120
5	40	235
6	35	225
7	20	160
8	25	200
9	33	220
10	19	120

The regression equation is:

$$sales = 61.296 + 4.706 \text{ (advertising expenses)}$$

1. What is the predicted sales volume for an advertising budget of $22,000?

2. What is the predicted sales volume if we spend $80,000?

3. Do you see a problem with an $80,000 budget? Why or why not?

_____

_____

_____

4. Describe the implications of using your linear regression model if the advertising sales relationship looks like that illustrated below. Show graphically where the prediction error is.

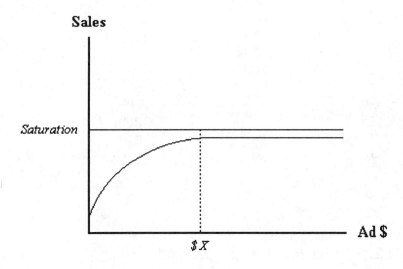

Module 10

SPSS PC+

Files and Special Keys

The following is a brief introduction to the use of SPSS/PC+. For further information, please consult one of the excellent books on SPSS by Norusis. A suggested starter book is *The SPSS Guide to Data Analysis for SPSS/PC+, 2nd edition.*

How it works: a conceptual overview.

Data Input >>>>>>>>>>SPSS PROGRAM >>>>>>>>>>>>>>>>>>> OUTPUT (results)

```
                    ^
                    ^
                    ^
            Instruction Input
```

Files:

Data input files:

FILE TYPE	COMMAND TO INPUT	CREATED BY
ASCII - Human readable files	Data List	WP or text editor
.WK1 - LOTUS 123 file	Translate from	Lotus123, Excel
.SPS - SPSS data file	GET	SPSS save Command
.SYS - SAME AS .sps " " " "	GET	SPSS save Command
.dbf - Dbase	Translate from	Dbase program

Program files:

ASCII only - Human readable-includes in Lower window of spss

F3 key in SPSS will allow input from files (make sure menu option is off)

Output files:

.Log - ASCII file with a list of all commands (instructions) that are run during the LAST session (does not include results)

.lis - ASCII file that includes output or results of running commands

Scratch.pad - last instruction set that was used (you should use the F9 key to save your program (instruction set) under a different name (prefer a:????.PRG)

Special Keys and their PRIMARY use:
F1 - lists files or variables located on disk
F2 - changes window structure
F3 - inserts files (I don't use this often)
F4 - Inserts lines (I don't use this often)
F5 - Looks up letters in the window (searches for specific letters)
F6 - Moves cursor
F7 - Marks an area or line for further use (same as F12 in WP)
F8 - Copy, Move or Delete lines marked by F7 command
F9 - SAVES INSTRUCTION SET -- **DO THIS OFTEN**
F10 - Runs instructions starting at cursor

alt-m - Toggles the menu on and off
alt-e - Moves the cursor from the menu to the lower window
alt-v - Shows you a list of the variables that can be used
alt-x - Allows for extended menu (more specific commands)

Windows
Menu - This allows you to write a program by choosing the appropriate command

Lower window - this includes the instruction set

Upper window - Shows the results of what has been run
(When menus are on part of this is hidden from view).

STATISTICS COMMANDS

The following example will walk you through the entire series of commands necessary to extract information from the case dealing with airline preference--Case B in the appendix of *Contemporary Marketing Research, 2nd ed.*, McDaniel and Gates. You will be expected to handle the other cases on your own using this information as a guide.

NOTE: The punctuation marks in the lines of code are important. If you see a period or a space, it is there for a reason. Input the information EXACTLY as you see it to reduce the possibility of error.

First the data must be read into the program :

GET /FILE 'a:airline.sps'.

The file for the output should be clearly identified :

set /LISTING 'a:air_stat.out'.

Always run descriptive statistics to make sure the file is in proper order - there is no substitute for visual examination.

DESCRIPTIVES /VARIABLES ALL.

CHI SQUARED STATISTICS (command CROSSTABS)

NOTE: Chi-Squared statistics should NOT be run on variables with high numbers of categories, nor should they be run on MANY pairs of variables--this will create excessive output.

ALSO NOTE: you must include the STATISTICS= CHISQ command.

CROSSTABS /TABLES= Q1 BY Q12 Q10 Q9 Q8 /STATISTICS= CHISQ.

CROSSTABS /TABLES= Q2 BY Q12 Q10 Q9 Q8 /STATISTICS= CHISQ.

t-TESTS (tests for differences in means)

NOTE: t-tests REQUIRE at least interval data. In this (and most other) studies, Likert scales will be assumed interval. (the t-test command also provides correlation values and their significance).

t-tests between 2 different variables

> T-TEST /PAIRS Q5A WITH Q5B Q5C Q5E Q5F.

t-tests on same variable between two different groups (e.g. male and female)

> T-TEST /GROUPS Q12 (1,2) /VARIABLES Q5A Q5B Q5C Q5E Q5F.

ANOVA (Analysis of Variance)

ANOVA tests differences in variables with respect to several groups, unlike a t-test that only tests differences between two groups.

The next line of code will give the same results as the t-test (above) because it is only testing 2 variables.

> ANOVA /VARIABLES Q5A Q5B Q5C Q5E Q5F BY Q12 (1,2).

The line of code below will examine the psychographic variables by education instead of gender.

> ANOVA /VARIABLES Q5A Q5B Q5C Q5E Q5F BY Q8 (1,9).

ENTERING THE DATA INTO THE SPSS PROGRAM

Step 1: The Data List command pulls the data into the program. In this case, it is drawing it from the case files.

```
DATA LIST FILE 'a:airtravl.out' FIXED /id_num 1-4
job_num 5
q1 6
q2 7
q3a 8-9 q3b 10-11 q3c 12-13 q3d 14-15 q3e 16-17
q4a 18-19 q4b 20-21 q4c 22-23 q4d 24-25 q4e 26-27
q5 28 q5a 29 q5b 30 q5c 31 q5d 32 q5e 33 q5f 34 q5g 35 q5h 36 q5i 37 q5j 38
q5k 39 q5l 40 q5m 41 q5n 42 q5o 43
q6 44-45
q7 46-47
q8 48-49
q9 50
q10 51
q11 52-53
q12 54
trips 70-73
record 80.
```

Step 2: set /listing - tells the computer where to write an output file.

```
SET /LISTING 'a:airline.prt'.
```

Step 3: The Descriptives command shows various basic statistics of variables.

```
DESCRIPTIVES /VARIABLES ALL.
```

Step 4: The Frequencies command shows the distribution of the data.

NOTE: use frequencies command on only nominal or ordinal data.

```
FREQUENCIES /VARIABLES Q1 Q2 Q3A Q4A Q5A Q6 Q7 Q8 Q9 Q10 Q11 Q12.
```

Step 5: Variable Labels creates proper labels for the variables--this is done so that the variables can be easily identified later. Other people looking at your data may have no idea what FPOP means if you don't write out a label explaining it.

VARIABLE LABELS

Q1 'business trips'
Q2 'personal trips'
Q3A 'airline' Q3B 'airline' Q3C 'airline' Q3D 'airline'
Q3E 'airline'
Q4A 'leisure activity' Q4B 'leisure activity'
Q4C 'leisure activity' Q4D 'leisure activity'
Q4E 'leisure activity'
Q5A 'psychographic1' Q5B 'psychographic2' Q5C 'psychographic3'
Q5D 'psychographic4' Q5E 'psychographic5' Q5F 'psychographic6'
Q5G 'psychographic7' Q5H 'psychographic8' Q5I 'psychographic9'
Q5J 'psychographic10' Q5K 'psychographic11' Q5L psychographic12'
Q5M 'psychographic13' Q5N 'psychographic14' Q5O psychographic15'
Q6 'household size'
Q7 'age'
Q8 'education'
Q9 'employment'
Q10 'marital status'
Q11 'income level'
Q12 'gender'
TRIPS 'number of trips'.

Step 6: Value labels creates names for specific values of a variable so that the meaning of the numbers is easily interpreted.

NOTE: this is only used for nominal and ordinal variables.

VALUE LABELS Q1 to Q2 1 'one trip' 2 'two trips' 3 '3-4 trips' 4 '5-10 trips' 5 '11-25 trips' 6 '26 + trips' 7 'do not know' 8 'refused'
/Q3A to Q3E 1 'United' 2 'American' 3 'Delta' 4 'Continental' 5 'Midway' 6 'Northwest'
7 'US Air'
8 'Braniff' 9 'Pan Am' 10 'TWA' 11 'Mexicana' 12 'Eastern' 13 'Piedmont' 14 'other'
15 'refused'
/Q4A to Q4E 1 'hunting/fishing' 2 'team sports' 3 'jogging' 4 'swimming' 5 'camping'
6 'golf' 7 'workout' 8 'cycling' 9 'tennis' 10 'boating' 11 'bowling' 12 'waterski'
13 'snowski' 14 'read' 15 'TV' 16 'travel' 17 'movies' 18 'sewing' 19 'art/craft' 20 'shopping' 21
'music' 22 'sightseeing' 23 'sporting events' 24 'video' 25 'yardwork' 26 'socializing'
27 'children' 28 'organizations' 29 'house projects' 30 'decorating' 31 'other'
32 'do not know'
/Q5A to Q5O 1 'Strongly disagree' 2 'somewhat disagree' 3 'neutral' 4 'somewhat agree'
5 'strongly agree'
/Q6 9 '9 or more people' 10 'refused'

/Q7 1 '18-24' 2 '25-29' 3 '30-34' 4 '35-39' 5 '40-44' 6 '45-49' 7 '50-54' 8 '55-59' 9 '60-64'
10 '65 and over' 11 'refused'
/Q8 1 'grade school' 2 'some high school' 3 'HS grad' 4 'community college' 5 'vo-tech'
6 'college < 4yrs' 7 'college grad' 8 'some post-grad' 9 'grad degree' 10 'refused'
/Q9 1 'full-time' 2 'retired' 3 'part-time' 4 'homemaker' 5 'student' 6 'unemployed' 7 'refused'
/Q10 1 'married' 2 'single' 3 'divorced' 4 'widowed' 5 'refused'
/Q11 1 '< 10K' 2 '10-15K' 3 '15-20K' 4 '20-25K' 5 '25-30K'
6 '30-40K' 7 '40-50K' 8 '50-75K' 9 '75-100K' 10 '100-150K'
11 'over 150K' 12 'refused' 13 'refused < 40K' 14 'refused > 40K'
/Q12 1 'male' 2 'female'.

Step 7: Examine the difference in output between the descriptives command before and after
using variable and value labels.

DESCRIPTIVES /VARIABLES ALL.
FREQUENCIES /VARIABLES Q1 Q2 Q3A Q4A Q5A Q6 Q7 Q8 Q9 Q10 Q11 Q12.

Step 8: The SAVE command allows all changes to the data
to be saved in SPSS format.

SAVE /OUTFILE 'a:airline.sps'.

OUTPUT: AIRLINE PREFERENCE CASE

The following section is the output from SPSS/PC+ for the airline preference case.

Always run descriptive statistics to make sure the file is in proper order--there is no substitute for visual examination.

```
DESCRIPTIVES /VARIABLES ALL.
-------------------------------------------------------------------
```

Number of Valid Observations (Listwise) =   2.00

Variable	Mean	Std Dev	Minimum	Maximum	N	Label
ID_NUM	700.50	404.29	1	1400	1400	
JOB_NUM	2.00	.00	2	2	1400	
Q1	6.70	2.30	1	8	1400	
business trips						
Q2	5.24	2.99	1	8	1400	
personal trips						
Q3A	4.29	4.51	1	15	776	airline
Q3B	5.84	4.03	1	14	295	airline
Q3C	6.85	4.13	1	14	107	airline
Q3D	7.61	3.94	1	14	41	airline
Q3E	10.42	3.45	5	14	12	airline
Q4A	16.20	9.31	1	32	1400	leisure
activity						
Q4B	16.39	8.89	1	31	1034	leisure
activity						
Q4C	17.06	8.85	1	31	631	leisure
activity						
Q4D	17.63	8.76	1	31	339	leisure
activity						
Q4E	19.11	8.32	1	31	174	leisure
activity						
Q5	1.00	.00	1	1	1400	
Q5A	3.48	1.49	1	5	1400	
psychographic1						
Q5B	2.86	1.49	1	5	1400	
psychographic2						
Q5C	2.88	1.50	1	5	1400	
psychographic3						
Q5D	3.34	1.58	1	5	1400	
psychographic4						
Q5E	3.53	1.37	1	5	1400	
psychographic5						
Q5F	3.60	1.52	1	5	1400	
psychographic6						
Q5G	2.61	1.46	1	5	1400	
psychographic7						

Q5I	3.12	1.51	1	5	1400	
psychographic9						
Q5J	2.55	1.60	1	5	1400	
psychographic10						
Q5K	3.01	1.53	1	5	1400	
psychographic11						
Q5L	3.66	1.34	1	5	1400	
psychographic12						
Q5M	1.83	1.26	1	5	1400	
psychographic13						
Q5N	3.42	1.34	1	5	1400	
psychographic14						
Q5O	2.72	1.43	1	5	1400	
psychographic15						
Q6	2.81	1.50	1	10	1400	
household size						
Q7	4.78	2.98	1	11	1400	age
Q8	5.26	2.20	1	10	1400	
education						
Q9	2.17	1.62	1	7	1400	
employment						
Q10	3.10	1.24	1	5	1400	marital
status						
Q11	7.15	3.11	1	14	1400	income
level						

```
Number of Valid Observations (Listwise) =          2.00

Variable      Mean     Std Dev   Minimum   Maximum      N  Label

Q12           1.52        .50         1         2   1400  gender
TRIPS         3.32       7.01         0        72   1400  number
of trips
RECORD        1.00        .00         1         1   1400
------------------------------------------------------------------
```

CHI SQUARED STATISTICS   (command CROSSTABS)

NOTE: Chi-Squared statistics should NOT be run on variables with high numbers of categories, nor should they be run on MANY pairs of variables—this will create excessive output.

ALSO NOTE: you must include the STATISTICS= CHISQ command.

CROSSTABS /TABLES= Q1 BY Q12 Q10 Q9 Q8 /STATISTICS= CHISQ.

Memory allows for 13,106 cells with 2 dimensions for general CROSSTABS.

(Some crosstabs are run here for illustration. They are not exhaustive, but do show some comparisons that are of interest to the researcher.)

```
------------------------------------------------------------------
```

Q1 business trips by Q12 gender

```
                   Q12
          Count  ³
                 ³ male      female
                 ³                        Row
                 ³     1 ³      2 ³  Total
Q1        ÄÄÄÄÄÄÄÄÄÄÅÄÄÄÄÄÄÄÄÄÄÄÅÄÄÄÄÄÄÄÄÄÄ´
          1    ³    37 ³     39 ³     76
 one trip      ³       ³        ³      5.4
               ÄÄÄÄÄÄÄÄÄÄÄÅÄÄÄÄÄÄÄÄÄÄÄ´
          2    ³    46 ³     30 ³     76
 two trips     ³       ³        ³      5.4
               ÄÄÄÄÄÄÄÄÄÄÄÅÄÄÄÄÄÄÄÄÄÄÄ´
          3    ³    47 ³     19 ³     66
 3-4 trips     ³       ³        ³      4.7
               ÄÄÄÄÄÄÄÄÄÄÄÅÄÄÄÄÄÄÄÄÄÄÄ´
          4    ³    46 ³     28 ³     74
 5-10 trips    ³       ³        ³      5.3
               ÀÄÄÄÄÄÄÄÄÄÄÁÄÄÄÄÄÄÄÄÄÄÄÙ
          Column    666     734    1400
(Continued) Total   47.6    52.4   100.0
```

Q1 business trips by Q12 gender

```
                    Q12
          Count  ³
                 ³ male        female
                 ³                         Row
                 ³     1  ³      2  ³    Total
Q1        ÄÄÄÄÄÄÄÄÄÄÅÄÄÄÄÄÄÄÄÄÄÅÄÄÄÄÄÄÄÄÄÄÄ´
              5  ³    28  ³      5  ³      33
  11-25 trips    ³         ³         ³     2.4
                 ÄÄÄÄÄÄÄÄÄÄÄÅÄÄÄÄÄÄÄÄÄÄ´
              6  ³    22  ³      4  ³      26
  26 + trips     ³         ³         ³     1.9
                 ÄÄÄÄÄÄÄÄÄÄÄÅÄÄÄÄÄÄÄÄÄÄ´
              7  ³    21  ³     28  ³      49
  do not know    ³         ³         ³     3.5
                 ÄÄÄÄÄÄÄÄÄÄÄÅÄÄÄÄÄÄÄÄÄÄ´
              8  ³   419  ³    581  ³    1000
  refused        ³         ³         ³    71.4
                 ÄÄÄÄÄÄÄÄÄÄÄÄÄÄÄÄÄÄÄÄÄÄÙ
       Column       666         734      1400
        Total       47.6        52.4     100.0
```

Chi-Square	Value	DF	Significance
Pearson	72.28173	7	.00000
Likelihood Ratio	75.58678	7	.00000
Mantel-Haenszel test for linear association	31.22770	1	.00000

Minimum Expected Frequency - 12.369

Number of Missing Observations: 0

Q1 business trips by Q10 marital status

```
                   Q10
   Count    ³
           ³married  single   divorced widowed  refused
            ³
                                                         Row       ³
            1  ³     2  ³     3  ³     4  ³     5  ³ Total
Q1         ÄÄÄÄÄÄÄÄÄÅÄÄÄÄÄÄÄÄÄÅÄÄÄÄÄÄÄÄÄÅÄÄÄÄÄÄÄÄÄÅÄÄÄÄÄÄÄÄÄ´
    1  ³     14  ³     3  ³    11  ³    46  ³     2  ³    76
  one trip        ³         ³         ³         ³         ³    5.4
           ÃÄÄÄÄÄÄÄÄÄÅÄÄÄÄÄÄÄÄÄÅÄÄÄÄÄÄÄÄÄÅÄÄÄÄÄÄÄÄÄÅÄÄÄÄÄÄÄÄÄ´
    2  ³     16  ³     1  ³    11  ³    48  ³         ³    76
  two trips       ³         ³         ³         ³         ³    5.4
           ÃÄÄÄÄÄÄÄÄÄÅÄÄÄÄÄÄÄÄÄÅÄÄÄÄÄÄÄÄÄÅÄÄÄÄÄÄÄÄÄÅÄÄÄÄÄÄÄÄÄ´
    3  ³     13  ³     2  ³    12  ³    39  ³         ³    66
  3-4 trips       ³         ³         ³         ³         ³    4.7
           ÃÄÄÄÄÄÄÄÄÄÅÄÄÄÄÄÄÄÄÄÅÄÄÄÄÄÄÄÄÄÅÄÄÄÄÄÄÄÄÄÅÄÄÄÄÄÄÄÄÄ´
    4  ³     15  ³         ³    12  ³    47  ³         ³    74
  5-10 trips      ³         ³         ³         ³         ³    5.3
           ÃÄÄÄÄÄÄÄÄÄÁÄÄÄÄÄÄÄÄÄÁÄÄÄÄÄÄÄÄÄÁÄÄÄÄÄÄÄÄÄÁÄÄÄÄÄÄÄÄÄÙ
    Column    305        84       184       819         8   1400
    Total     21.8       6.0      13.1      58.5        .6  100.0
```

Q1 business trips by Q10 marital status

```
                   Q10
   Count    ³
           ³married  single   divorced widowed  refused
            ³
                                                         Row
            1  ³     2  ³     3  ³     4  ³     5  ³ Total
Q1         ÄÄÄÄÄÄÄÄÄÅÄÄÄÄÄÄÄÄÄÅÄÄÄÄÄÄÄÄÄÅÄÄÄÄÄÄÄÄÄÅÄÄÄÄÄÄÄÄÄ´
            5  ³     6  ³     7  ³    20  ³    33  ³
  11-25 trips     ³         ³         ³         ³         ³    2.4
           ÃÄÄÄÄÄÄÄÄÄÅÄÄÄÄÄÄÄÄÄÅÄÄÄÄÄÄÄÄÄÅÄÄÄÄÄÄÄÄÄÅÄÄÄÄÄÄÄÄÄ´
    6  ³      2  ³         ³     1  ³    23  ³         ³    26
  26 + trips      ³         ³         ³         ³         ³    1.9
           ÃÄÄÄÄÄÄÄÄÄÅÄÄÄÄÄÄÄÄÄÅÄÄÄÄÄÄÄÄÄÅÄÄÄÄÄÄÄÄÄÅÄÄÄÄÄÄÄÄÄ´
    7  ³     11  ³     1  ³     7  ³    30  ³         ³    49
  do not know     ³         ³         ³         ³         ³    3.5
           ÃÄÄÄÄÄÄÄÄÄÅÄÄÄÄÄÄÄÄÄÅÄÄÄÄÄÄÄÄÄÅÄÄÄÄÄÄÄÄÄÅÄÄÄÄÄÄÄÄÄ´
    8  ³    228  ³    77  ³   123  ³   566  ³     6  ³ 1000
  refused         ³         ³         ³         ³         ³   71.4
           ÃÄÄÄÄÄÄÄÄÄÁÄÄÄÄÄÄÄÄÄÁÄÄÄÄÄÄÄÄÄÁÄÄÄÄÄÄÄÄÄÁÄÄÄÄÄÄÄÄÄÙ
Column      305        84       184       819         8    1400
Total       21.8       6.0      13.1      58.5        .6   100.0
```

```
Chi-Square                      Value       DF       Significance
----------                      -----       ----     ------------

Pearson                         40.84038    28       .05554
Likelihood Ratio                50.15173    28       .00622
Mantel-Haenszel test for        4.76982     1        .02896
        linear association


Minimum Expected Frequency -        .149
Cells with Expected Frequency < 5 -     16 OF     40 ( 40.0%)


Number of Missing Observations:   0
```

Q1 business trips by Q9 employment

```
                        Q9
   Count  ³
          ³full-time retired  part-time homemaker student
                    ³                                              Row
          ³    1   ³    2   ³    3   ³    4   ³    5   ³  Total
Q1         ÄÄÄÄÄÄÄÄÄÄÄÄÄÄÄÄÄÄÄÄÄÄÄÄÄÄÄÄÄÄÄÄÄÄÄÄÄÄÄÄÄÄÄÄÄÄÄÄÄÄÄÄÄÄÄ´
     1   ³    57  ³    9   ³        ³        ³    3   ³   76
   one trip      ³        ³        ³        ³        ³    5.4
           ÄÄÄÄÄÄÄÄÄÄÄÄÄÄÄÄÄÄÄÄÄÄÄÄÄÄÄÄÄÄÄÄÄÄÄÄÄÄÄÄÄÄÄÄÄÄÄÄÄÄÄÄÄÄÄ´
     2   ³    58  ³    7   ³    6   ³    2   ³        ³   76
   two trips     ³        ³        ³        ³        ³    5.4
           ÄÄÄÄÄÄÄÄÄÄÄÄÄÄÄÄÄÄÄÄÄÄÄÄÄÄÄÄÄÄÄÄÄÄÄÄÄÄÄÄÄÄÄÄÄÄÄÄÄÄÄÄÄÄÄ´
     3   ³    56  ³    4   ³        ³    4   ³    2   ³   66
   3-4 trips     ³        ³        ³        ³        ³    4.7
           ÄÄÄÄÄÄÄÄÄÄÄÄÄÄÄÄÄÄÄÄÄÄÄÄÄÄÄÄÄÄÄÄÄÄÄÄÄÄÄÄÄÄÄÄÄÄÄÄÄÄÄÄÄÄÄ´
     4   ³    58  ³    10  ³    2   ³    2   ³    2   ³   74
   5-10 trips    ³        ³        ³        ³        ³    5.3
           ÄÄÄÄÄÄÄÄÄÄÄÄÄÄÄÄÄÄÄÄÄÄÄÄÄÄÄÄÄÄÄÄÄÄÄÄÄÄÄÄÄÄÄÄÄÄÄÄÄÄÄÄÄÄÄÙ
Column       795      158      151      63       181     1400
 Total       56.8     11.3     10.8     4.5      12.9    100.0
```

Q1 business trips by Q9 employment

		Q9		
Count		unemployed	refused	Row
		6	7	Total
Q1				
one trip	1	5	2	76 5.4
two trips	2	3		76 5.4
3-4 trips	3			66 4.7
5-10 trips	4			74 5.3
(Continued)	Column Total	46 3.3	6 .4	1400 100.0

Q1 business trips by Q9 employment

		Q9				
Count		full-time	retired	part-time	homemaker	student	
		1	2	3	4	5	Row Total
Q1							
11-25 trips	5	28	4			1	33 2.4
26 + trips	6	21	2	2		1	26 1.9
do not know	7	22	8	8	3	6	49 3.5
refused	8	495	114	133	52	166	1000 71.4
Column Total		795 56.8	158 11.3	151 10.8	63 4.5	181 12.9	1400 100.0

Q1 business trips by Q9 employment

	Q9		
Count	unemployed	refused	
	6	7	Row Total
Q1			
11-25 trips 5			33 2.4
26 + trips 6			26 1.9
do not know 7	2		49 3.5
refused 8	36	4	1000 71.4
Column Total	46 3.3	6 .4	1400 100.0

Chi-Square	Value	DF	Significance
Pearson	146.29368	42	.00000
Likelihood Ratio	190.11227	42	.00000
Mantel-Haenszel test for linear association	66.34078	1	.00000

Minimum Expected Frequency -   .111
Cells with Expected Frequency < 5 -   28 OF   56 (50.0%)

Number of Missing Observations: 0

Q1 business trips by Q8 education

Q8

Count	grade school	some high school	high school graduate	community college	vo-tech	Row Total
	1	2	3	4	5	
Q1						
1 one trip		4	18	5	2	76 / 5.4
2 two trips		2	8	6	4	76 / 5.4
3 3-4 trips		2	4	2	1	66 / 4.7
4 5-10 trips			11		6	74 / 5.3
Column Total	20 / 1.4	110 / 7.9	354 / 25.3	70 / 5.0	57 / 4.1	1400 / 100.0

Q1 business trips by Q8 education

Q8

Count	college < 4yrs	college grad	some post-grad	grad degree	refused	Row Total
	6	7	8	9	10	
Q1						
1 one trip	15	24	3	5		76 5.4
2 two trips	11	23	3	19		76 5.4
3 3-4 trips	15	22	7	11	2	66 4.7
4 5-10 trips	18	24	1	14		74 5.3
Column Total	355 25.4	252 18.0	46 3.3	123 8.8	13 .9	1400 100.0

Q1 business trips by Q8 education

Q8

Count	grade school	some high school	high school graduate	community college	vo-tech	Row Total
Q1	1	2	3	4	5	
5 11-25 trips			6			33 2.4
6 26 + trips			1			26 1.9
7 do not know		1	18	1	2	49 3.5
8 refused	20	101	288	56	42	1000 71.4
Column Total	20 1.4	110 7.9	354 25.3	70 5.0	57 4.1	1400 100.0

96

Q1 business trips by Q8 education

Q8

Count	college < 4yrs	college grad	some post-grad	grad degree	refused	Row Total
	6	7	8	9	10	
Q1						
5 11-25 trips	4	14	2	7		33 / 2.4
6 26 + trips	5	8	3	9		26 / 1.9
7 do not know	12	8	3	3	1	49 / 3.5
8 refused	275	129	24	55	10	1000 / 71.4
Column Total	355 / 25.4	252 / 18.0	46 / 3.3	123 / 8.8	13 / .9	1400 / 100.0

Chi-Square	Value	DF	Significance
Pearson	253.07349	63	.00000
Likelihood Ratio	258.43322	63	.00000
Mantel-Haenszel test for linear association	89.42575	1	.00000

Minimum Expected Frequency - .241
Cells with Expected Frequency < 5 - 42 OF 80 (52.5%)

Number of Missing Observations: 0

CROSSTABS /TABLES= Q2 BY Q12 Q10 Q9 Q8 /STATISTICS= CHISQ.

Memory allows for 13,106 cells with 2 dimensions for general CROSSTABS.

Q2 personal trips by Q12 gender

Count	Q12		
	male	female	Row
	1	2	Total
Q2			
1	113	127	240
one trip			17.1
2	76	95	171
two trips			12.2
3	76	74	150
3-4 trips			10.7
4	47	35	82
5-10 trips			5.9
Column	666	734	1400
(Continued) Total	47.6	52.4	100.0

Q2 personal trips by Q12 gender

Count	Q12		
	male	female	Row
	1	2	Total
Q2			
5	8	7	15
11-25 trips			1.1
6		3	3
26 + trips			.2
7	12	13	25
do not know			1.8
8	334	380	714
refused			51.0
Column	666	734	1400
Total	47.6	52.4	100.0

Chi-Square	Value	DF	Significance
Pearson	7.49562	7	.37916
Likelihood Ratio	8.64876	7	.27887
Mantel-Haenszel test for linear association	.06963	1	.79188

Minimum Expected Frequency -   1.427
Cells with Expected Frequency < 5 -   2 OF   16 (12.5%)

Number of Missing Observations: 0

Q2 personal trips by Q9 employment

Q9

```
Count   ³
        ³full-time retired  part-time homemaker student
                                                      Row
        ³    1   ³    2   ³    3   ³    4   ³    5   ³ Total
Q2       ÄÄÄÄÄÄÄÄÄÄÅÄÄÄÄÄÄÄÄÄÄÅÄÄÄÄÄÄÄÄÄÄÅÄÄÄÄÄÄÄÄÄÄÅÄÄÄÄÄÄÄÄÄÄÅÄÄÄÄÄÄÄÄÄ
    1   ³   139  ³    23  ³    28  ³    17  ³    24  ³   240
  one trip      ³        ³        ³        ³        ³   17.1
         ÄÄÄÄÄÄÄÄÄÄÅÄÄÄÄÄÄÄÄÄÄÅÄÄÄÄÄÄÄÄÄÄÅÄÄÄÄÄÄÄÄÄÄÅÄÄÄÄÄÄÄÄÄÄÅÄÄÄÄÄÄÄÄÄ
    2   ³   108  ³    16  ³    17  ³     9  ³    16  ³   171
  two trips     ³        ³        ³        ³        ³   12.2
         ÄÄÄÄÄÄÄÄÄÄÅÄÄÄÄÄÄÄÄÄÄÅÄÄÄÄÄÄÄÄÄÄÅÄÄÄÄÄÄÄÄÄÄÅÄÄÄÄÄÄÄÄÄÄÅÄÄÄÄÄÄÄÄÄ
    3   ³    92  ³    19  ³    10  ³     6  ³    23  ³   150
  3-4 trips     ³        ³        ³        ³        ³   10.7
         ÄÄÄÄÄÄÄÄÄÄÅÄÄÄÄÄÄÄÄÄÄÅÄÄÄÄÄÄÄÄÄÄÅÄÄÄÄÄÄÄÄÄÄÅÄÄÄÄÄÄÄÄÄÄÅÄÄÄÄÄÄÄÄÄ
    4   ³    48  ³    14  ³     6  ³     6  ³     6  ³    82
  5-10 trips    ³        ³        ³        ³        ³    5.9
         ÀÄÄÄÄÄÄÄÄÄÁÄÄÄÄÄÄÄÄÄÄÁÄÄÄÄÄÄÄÄÄÄÁÄÄÄÄÄÄÄÄÄÄÁÄÄÄÄÄÄÄÄÄÄÙ
Column     795       158       151        63       181      1400
 Total     56.8      11.3      10.8       4.5      12.9     100.0
```

Q2   personal trips   by   Q9   employment

<pre>
                   Q9
           Count ³
                  ³ unemployed refused
                  ³   Row
                  ³   6   ³   7   ³   Total
Q2
                1 ³   7   ³   2   ³   240
   one trip   ³   ³   ³   17.1

                2 ³   3   ³   2   ³   171
   two trips   ³   ³   ³   12.2

                3 ³   ³   ³   150
   3-4 trips   ³   ³   ³   10.7

                4 ³   2   ³   ³   82
   5-10 trips   ³   ³   ³   5.9

           Column   46   6   1400
(Continued) Total   3.3   .4   100.0
</pre>

Q2 personal trips by Q9 employment

<pre>
                        Q9

Count ³
       ³ full-time retired part-time homemaker student
                                                              Row
       ³   1   ³   2   ³   3   ³   4   ³   5   ³   Total
Q2
5   ³   11   ³   3   ³   ³   ³   1   ³   15
 11-25 trips   ³   ³   ³   ³   ³   1.1

6   ³   2   ³   ³   1   ³   ³   ³   3
 26 + trips   ³   ³   ³   ³   ³   .2

7   ³   13   ³   6   ³   1   ³   ³   4   ³   25
 do not know   ³   ³   ³   ³   ³   1.8

8   ³ 382   ³   77   ³   88   ³   25   ³ 107   ³   714
 refused   ³   ³   ³   ³   ³   51.0

Column   795   158   151   63   181   1400
 Total   56.8   11.3   10.8   4.5   12.9   100.0
</pre>

Q2 **personal trips** by Q9 **employment**

```
                     Q9
          Count  ³
                 ³ unemployed refused
                                        Row
                 ³    6    ³    7    ³  Total
Q2        ÄÄÄÄÄÄÄÄÄÄÄÄÄÄÄÄÄÄÄÄÄÄÄÄÄÄÄÄÄ´
             5   ³         ³         ³    15
 11-25 trips     ³         ³         ³   1.1
          ÄÄÄÄÄÄÄÄÄÄÄÄÄÄÄÄÄÄÄÄÄ´
             6   ³         ³         ³     3
 26 + trips      ³         ³         ³    .2
          ÃÄÄÄÄÄÄÄÄÄÄÄÄÄÄÄÄÄÄÄÄ´
             7   ³    1    ³         ³    25
 do not know     ³         ³         ³   1.8
          ÃÄÄÄÄÄÄÄÄÄÄÄÄÄÄÄÄÄÄÄÄ´
             8   ³   33    ³    2    ³   714
 refused         ³         ³         ³  51.0
          ÀÄÄÄÄÄÄÄÄÄÄÄÄÄÄÄÄÄÄÄÄÄÄÄÄÙ
          Column     46         6      1400
          Total      3.3        .4    100.0
```

Chi-Square	Value	DF	Significance
Pearson	56.01111	42	.07260
Likelihood Ratio	64.75834	42	.01361
Mantel-Haenszel test for linear association	7.28224	1	.00696

Minimum Expected Frequency -   .013
Cells with Expected Frequency < 5 -   27 OF   56 (48.2%)

Number of Missing Observations: 0

t-TESTS   (tests for differences in means)

NOTE: t-tests REQUIRE at least interval data--in this (and most other) studies, Likert scales will be assumed interval. The t-test command also provides correlation values and their significance.

* t-tests between 2 different variables *

T-TEST /PAIRS Q5A WITH Q5B Q5C Q5E Q5F.
T-TEST requires 256 BYTES of workspace for execution.

- - - t-tests for paired samples - - -

Variable	Number of pairs	Corr	2-tail Sig	Mean	SD	SE of Mean
Q5A psychographic1				3.4821	1.491	.040
	1400	.062	.021			
Q5B psychographic2				2.8550	1.492	.040

Mean	SD	Paired Differences SE of Mean	t-value	df	2-tail Sig
.6271	2.044	.055	11.48	1399	.000

95% CI (.520, .734)

- - - t-tests for paired samples - - -

Variable	Number of pairs	Corr	2-tail Sig	Mean	SD	SE of Mean
Q5A psychographic1				3.4821	1.491	.040
	1400	.079	.003			
Q5C psychographic3				2.8757	1.503	.040

Mean	SD	Paired Differences SE of Mean	t-value	df	2-tail Sig
.6064	2.032	.054	11.17	1399	.000

95% CI (.500, .713)

```
              - - - t-tests for paired samples - - -


              Number of         2-tail
Variable        pairs    Corr   Sig    Mean     SD    SE of Mean
ÄÄÄÄÄÄÄÄÄÄÄÄÄÄÄÄÄÄÄÄÄÄÄÄÄÄÄÄÄÄÄÄÄÄÄÄÄÄÄÄÄÄÄÄÄÄÄÄÄÄÄÄÄÄÄÄÄÄÄÄÄÄÄ

Q5A   psychographic1                 3.4821   1.491     .040
                 1400    .156   .000
Q5E   psychographic5                 3.5300   1.373     .037

ÄÄÄÄÄÄÄÄÄÄÄÄÄÄÄÄÄÄÄÄÄÄÄÄÄÄÄÄÄÄÄÄÄÄÄÄÄÄÄÄÄÄÄÄÄÄÄÄÄÄÄÄÄÄÄÄÄÄÄÄÄÄÄ


         Paired Differences          ³
Mean      SD       SE of Mean ³   t-value      df      2-tail Sig
ÄÄÄÄÄÄÄÄÄÄÄÄÄÄÄÄÄÄÄÄÄÄÄÄÄÄÄÄÄÄÄÄÄÄÄÄÄ³ ÄÄÄÄÄÄÄÄÄÄÄÄÄÄÄÄÄÄÄÄÄÄÄÄÄÄÄ
-.0479   1.863    .050      ³     -.96     1399         .337

95% CI (-.146, .050)                  ³
```

```
              - - - t-tests for paired samples - - -


              Number of         2-tail
Variable        pairs    Corr   Sig    Mean     SD    SE of Mean
ÄÄÄÄÄÄÄÄÄÄÄÄÄÄÄÄÄÄÄÄÄÄÄÄÄÄÄÄÄÄÄÄÄÄÄÄÄÄÄÄÄÄÄÄÄÄÄÄÄÄÄÄÄÄÄÄÄÄÄÄÄÄÄ
 Q5A   psychographic1                 3.4821   1.491     .040
                 1400    .061   .022
 Q5F   psychographic6                 3.5971   1.523     .041
ÄÄÄÄÄÄÄÄÄÄÄÄÄÄÄÄÄÄÄÄÄÄÄÄÄÄÄÄÄÄÄÄÄÄÄÄÄÄÄÄÄÄÄÄÄÄÄÄÄÄÄÄÄÄÄÄÄÄÄÄÄÄÄ


         Paired Differences            ³
Mean      SD       SE of Mean ³   t-value      df   2-tail Sig

ÄÄÄÄÄÄÄÄÄÄÄÄÄÄÄÄÄÄÄÄÄÄÄÄÄÄÄÄÄÄÄÄÄÄÄÄÄ³ ÄÄÄÄÄÄÄÄÄÄÄÄÄÄÄÄÄÄÄÄÄÄÄÄÄÄÄ

-.1150   2.065      .055      ³     -2.08     1399     .037

95% CI (-.223, -.007)                  ³
```

* t-tests on same variable between two different groups (e.g. male and female) *.

T-TEST /GROUPS Q12 (1,2) /VARIABLES Q5A Q5B Q5C Q5E Q5F.
T-TEST requires 360 BYTES of workspace for execution.

t-tests for independent samples of Q12   gender

Variable	Number of Cases	Mean	SD	SE of Mean
ÄÄ				
Q5A psychographic1				
male	666	3.5195	1.505	.058
female	734	3.4482	1.479	.055
ÄÄ				

Mean Difference = .0713

Levene's Test for Equality of Variances: F= .043

P= .835

t-test for Equality of Means

Variances	t-value	df	2-Tail Sig	SE of Diff	95% CI for Diff
ÄÄ					
Equal	.89	1398	.372	.080	(-.085, .228)
Unequal	.89	1379.85	.372	.080	(-.085, .228)
ÄÄ					

t-tests for independent samples of Q12   gender

Variable	Number of Cases	Mean	SD	SE of Mean
ÄÄ				
Q5B psychographic2				
male	666	2.9294	1.528	.059
female	734	2.7875	1.457	.054
ÄÄ				

Mean Difference = .1420

Levene's Test for Equality of Variances: F= 4.009

P= .045

      t-test for Equality of Means

Variances	t-value	df	2-Tail Sig	SE of Diff	95% CI for Diff

ÄÄ

Variances	t-value	df	2-Tail Sig	SE of Diff	95% CI for Diff
Equal	1.78	1398	.075	.080	(-.015, .299)
Unequal	1.77	1369.54	.076	.080	(-.015, .299)

ÄÄ

t-tests for independent samples of Q12   gender

Variable	Number of Cases	Mean	SD	SE of Mean

ÄÄ
Q5C psychographic3

Variable	Number of Cases	Mean	SD	SE of Mean
male	666	2.8213	1.452	.056
female	734	2.9251	1.546	.057

ÄÄ

Mean Difference = -.1037

Levene's Test for Equality of Variances: F= 11.642
P= .001

      t-test for Equality of Means

Variances	t-value	df	2-Tail Sig	SE of Diff	95% CI for Diff

ÄÄ
| Equal | -1.29 | 1398 | .197 | .080 | (-.261, .054) |
| Unequal | -1.29 | 1396.37 | .196 | .080 | (-.261, .054) |

ÄÄ
----

t-tests for independent samples of   Q12   gender

                    Number
Variable   of Cases   Mean   SD   SE of Mean

ÄÄÄ
Q5E psychographic5

male   666   3.6967   1.336   .052
female   734   3.3787   1.390   .051

ÄÄÄ

         Mean Difference = .3180

         Levene's Test for Equality of Variances: F= 13.435
                                                  P= .000

         t-test for Equality of Means
                                                       95%
Variances t-value   df   2-Tail Sig SE of Diff CI for
                                                   Diff

 ÄÄÄ
Equal   4.35   1398   .000   .073   (.175, .461)
Unequal   4.36   1393.40   .000   .073   (.175, .461)
 ÄÄÄ
----

t-tests for independent samples of   Q12   gender

                    Number
Variable   of Cases   Mean   SD   SE of Mean
 Q5F psychographic6

male   666   3.2583   1.548   .060
female   734   3.9046   1.433   .053

         Mean Difference = -.6464

         Levene's Test for Equality of Variances: F= 31.859
                                                  P= .000

         t-test for Equality of Means
                                                       95%
Variances t-value   df   2-Tail Sig SE of Diff CI for
                                                   Diff

Equal   -8.11   1398   .000   .080   (-.803, -.490)
Unequal   -8.08   1356.93   .000   .080   (-.803, -.489)

ANOVA (Analysis of Variance)

Tests differences in variables with respect to several groups--unlike t-test that only tests difference between two groups.

```
* This will give the same results as the t-test (above) *.
ANOVA /VARIABLES Q5A Q5B Q5C Q5E Q5F BY Q12 (1,2).
```

'ANOVA' PROBLEM REQUIRES   526 BYTES OF MEMORY.

* * * A N A L Y S I S   O F   V A R I A N C E * * *

	Q5A	psychographic1
BY	Q12	gender

Source of Variation	Sum of Squares	DF	Mean Square	F	Signif of F
Main Effects	1.775	1	1.775	.798	.372
Q12	1.775	1	1.775	.798	.372
Explained	1.775	1	1.775	.798	.372
Residual	3109.779	1398	2.224		
Total	3111.554	1399	2.224		

1400 Cases were processed.
   0 Cases (.0 PCT) were missing.

* * * A N A L Y S I S   O F   V A R I A N C E * * *

	Q5B	psychographic2
BY	Q12	gender

Source of Variation	Sum of Squares	DF	Mean Square	F	Signif of F
Main Effects	7.037	1	7.037	3.165	.075
Q12	7.037	1	7.037	3.165	.075
Explained	7.037	1	7.037	3.165	.075
Residual	3108.528	1398	2.224		
Total	3115.565	1399	2.227		

```
1400 Cases were processed.
   0 Cases (   .0 PCT) were missing.
     * * *  A N A L Y S I S   O F   V A R I A N C E  * * *


          Q5C        psychographic3
     BY   Q12        gender


Source of      Sum of                    Mean                  Signif
Variation      Squares        DF         Square        F       of F

Main Effects    3.758          1         3.758       1.666      .197
   Q12          3.758          1         3.758       1.666      .197

Explained       3.758          1         3.758       1.666      .197

Residual     3154.616       1398         2.257

Total        3158.374       1399         2.258



1400 Cases were processed.
   0 Cases (   .0 PCT) were missing.

     * * *  A N A L Y S I S   O F   V A R I A N C E  * * *

          Q5E        psychographic5
     BY   Q12        gender


Source of      Sum of                    Mean                  Signif
Variation      Squares        DF         Square        F       of F

Main Effects   35.299          1        35.299      18.955      .000
   Q12         35.299          1        35.299      18.955      .000

Explained      35.299          1        35.299      18.955      .000

Residual     2603.441       1398         1.862

Total        2638.740       1399         1.886
----------------------------------------------------------------------
```

```
* * *   A N A L Y S I S   O F   V A R I A N C E   * * *

            Q5F        psychographic6
     BY     Q12        gender

Source of        Sum of                    Mean                 Signif
Variation        Squares        DF         Square        F      of F

Main Effects     145.885        1          145.885       65.813  .000
    Q12          145.885        1          145.885       65.813  .000

Explained        145.885        1          145.885       65.813  .000

Residual         3098.904       1398       2.217

Total            3244.789       1399       2.319


   1400 Cases were processed.
      0 Cases (    .0 PCT) were missing.
```

* This will examine the psychographic variables by education instead of gender*.

ANOVA /VARIABLES Q5A Q5B Q5C Q5E Q5F BY Q8 (1,9).

'ANOVA' PROBLEM REQUIRES   2038 BYTES OF MEMORY.

* * *   A N A L Y S I S   O F   V A R I A N C E   * * *

```
        Q5A        psychographic1
   BY   Q8         education
```

Source of Variation	Sum of Squares	DF	Mean Square	F	Signif of F
Main Effects	128.567	8	16.071	7.462	.000
Q8	128.567	8	16.071	7.462	.000
Explained	128.567	8	16.071	7.462	.000
Residual	2967.677	1378	2.154		
Total	3096.244	1386	2.234		

1400 Cases were processed.
  13 Cases (.9 PCT) were missing.

* * *   A N A L Y S I S   O F   V A R I A N C E   * * *

```
        Q5B        psychographic2
   BY   Q8         education
```

Source of Variation	Sum of Squares	DF	Mean Square	F	Signif of F
Main Effects	150.179	8	18.772	8.807	.000
Q8	150.179	8	18.772	8.807	.000
Explained	150.179	8	18.772	8.807	.000
Residual	2937.110	1378	2.131		
Total	3087.289	1386	2.227		

1400 Cases were processed.
  13 Cases (.9 PCT) were missing.

```
          Q5C        psychographic3
      BY  Q8         education

Source of    Sum of                 Mean              Signif
Variation    Squares      DF         Square      F     of F

Main Effects  40.115       8         5.014     2.248    .022
   Q8         40.115       8         5.014     2.248    .022

Explained     40.115       8         5.014     2.248    .022

Residual    3073.475    1378         2.230

Total       3113.590    1386         2.246
```

1400 Cases were processed. 13 Cases (.9 PCT) were missing.

```
          Q5E        psychographic5
      BY  Q8         education

Source of    Sum of                 Mean              Signif
Variation    Squares      DF         Square      F     of F

Main Effects  27.021       8         3.378     1.791    .075
   Q8         27.021       8         3.378     1.791    .075

Explained     27.021       8         3.378     1.791    .075

Residual    2598.920    1378         1.886

Total       2625.941    1386         1.895
```

1400 Cases were processed. 13 Cases (.9 PCT) were missing.

```
          Q5F        psychographic6
      BY  Q8         education

Source of    Sum of                 Mean              Signif
Variation    Squares      DF         Square      F     of F

Main Effects  50.980       8         6.373     2.761    .005
   Q8         50.980       8         6.373     2.761    .005

Explained     50.980       8         6.373     2.761    .005

Residual    3180.232    1378         2.308

Total       3231.213    1386         2.331
FINISH.
```